£3.99

G000146231

DECORATED PAPERS AND CARDS

Hilary Devonshire

Consultant: Henry Pluckrose

Photography: Chris Fairclough

FRANKLIN WATTS
London/New York/Sydney/Toronto

Copyright © 1992 Franklin Watts

Franklin Watts
96-98 Leonard Street
London EC2A 4RH

Franklin Watts Australia
14 Mars Road
Lane Cove
NSW 2066

UK ISBN: 0 7496 0749 1

A CIP catalogue record
for this book is available
from the British Library

Design: Edward Kinsey

Editor: Jenny Wood

Typeset by Lineage Ltd,
Watford, England

Printed in Belgium

Contents

This book describes activities which use the following:

Adhesives – cold-water paste
          – glue (UHU glue sticks, Bostick Solvent-Free, Copydex))
          – adhesive pads

Assorted objects for printing (old kitchen utensils, corks, cotton reels, garden sticks, junk pieces)

Brushes – flat-headed brush for stencilling
        – old brushes (brush, nailbrush, toothbrush)
        – wide brush

Carbon paper

Card (thin white card and scraps of thick card)

Cardboard box (large)

Containers (small bowls or dishes, jam jars, old ice-cream cartons)

Craft knife

Diffuser spray

Dyes – cold-water dyes

Fork (old)

Glitter

Hole punch

Inks – drawing inks
     – marbling inks
     – printing inks, water-based

Leaves

Linseed oil (boiled)

Liquid detergent

Newspapers (separated sheets)

Paints – acrylic paints
      – poster or powder paints
      – water-colour paints

Paper – good quality typing paper
      – sugar or construction paper
      – white and coloured lining paper

Paper serviettes (or kitchen towels) (plain, white)

Pencil

Pens (felt-tip, gold and silver)

Printing roller

Printing sheet (or tile), (plastic)

Ribbon (or string or thread, for gift tag ties)

Ruler – metal, for use with craft knife
     – wooden or plastic

Scissors

Screen-printing frame and squeegee

Sponges (thin, flat)

Spoons (old)

Sugar

Tray (deep, for marbling)

Vinegar

Water

There are many different ways of producing decorated papers. With methods such as printing or stencilling, the basic design can be repeated many times. But with methods such as marbling, the pattern is captured only once and therefore has its own unique charm.

Much pleasure can be gained from successfully producing home-made papers, and they can be used for many purposes. Presents for friends and relatives can be wrapped in your own decorated papers and accompanied by a matching card or gift tag. Some ideas for cards and gift tags are included in the following pages.

As you work, you will discover how different materials behave, how thickly or thinly to use the paints, which are the most suitable inks or papers, and which tools are best. You will learn these things only by experimenting for yourself. Try to use the different techniques described in this book to develop new designs of your own. Turning an idea into something new is being truly creative. Have fun!

1 Some of the equipment and materials you will need when making the decorated papers and cards described in this book.

Using a coloured paste mix is an easy way of making colourful papers. Once you have covered your paper with a layer of colour, you can use all sorts of objects to create interesting patterns and designs.

You will need wallpaper paste, water, two mixing bowls or old ice-cream cartons, a spoon, paints, a teaspoonful of liquid detergent, a stick for stirring, sheets of newspaper, paper, a wide brush, and assorted objects with which to make a print.

1 Prepare some wallpaper paste, mixing until you achieve a creamy consistency. In a separate bowl, mix together some paint, the liquid detergent and a small amount of the ready-mixed wallpaper paste. Stir until smooth.

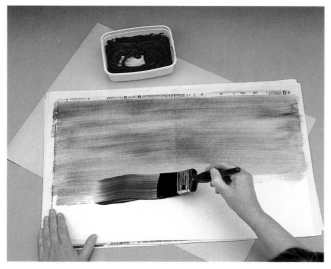

2 Arrange the sheets of newspaper into a pile, and place a sheet of paper on top. (The newspaper gives a soft surface for painting, and you can easily remove the top sheet if it becomes too sticky with paste.) Use long, quick strokes to brush the coloured paste across the paper. Work first in one direction ...

3 ... then in the other direction.

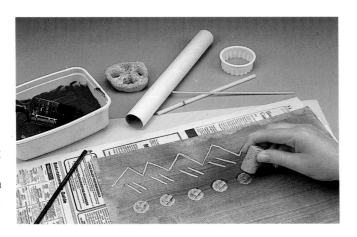

4 While the paste is still wet, use a piece of stick to scratch out a design, or press an object down on to the paste, then lift it away. The object will leave an impression of its shape. Here a cork is being used to create a design.

5 Here a pastry cutter is pressed into the paste, twisted...

6 ... and lifted away. A cotton reel is then pressed into the centre of each shape, to create an interesting pattern.

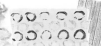

7 The finished design.

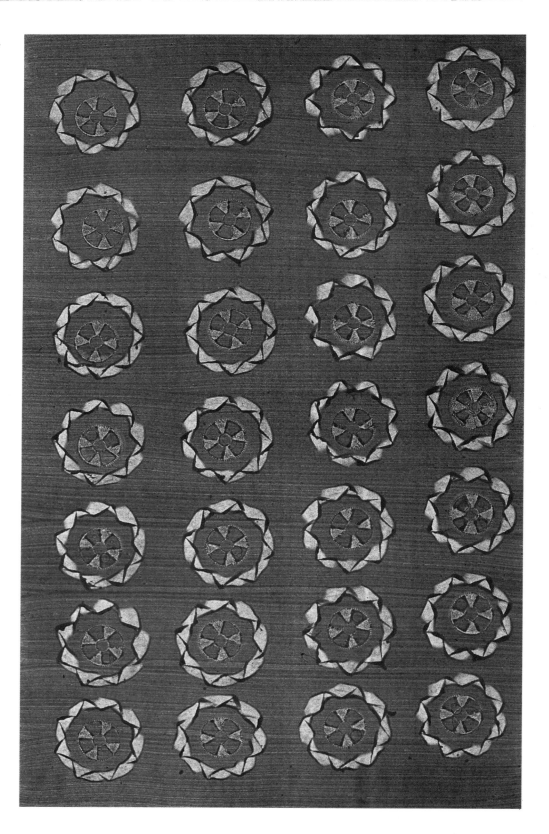

8 A selection of paste and paint papers.

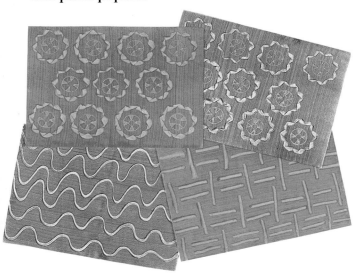

9 Instead of covering your sheet of paper with a wash of coloured paste, leave the paper white. Press your printing object (for example, the cotton reel or pastry cutter) into the coloured paste mix, then make a coloured pattern on the white paper.

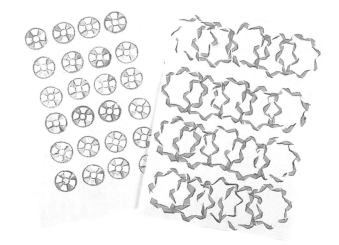

10 Use your decorated paper to wrap a gift and make a matching card.

Working with vinegar and sugar paste will give an unusual shine and texture to your finished designs.

You will need a mixture of malt vinegar and sugar (one part vinegar to two parts sugar), a jar (with a screw top), a spoon, a bowl or old ice-cream carton, water-colour paints, an old fork, sheets of newspaper, paper, a wide brush, and pieces of thick card.

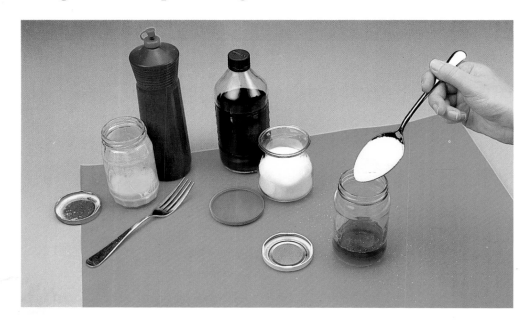

1 Put the sugar and vinegar into the jar.

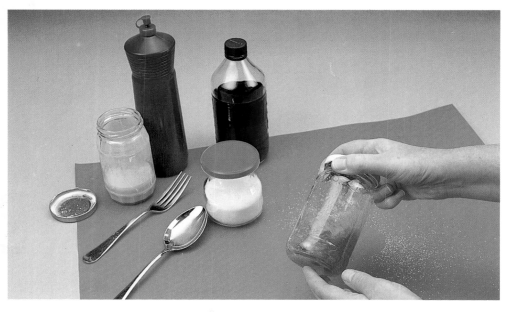

2 Screw the top of the jar on tightly, then shake the jar until the sugar and vinegar are well mixed.

3 Pour the mixture into the bowl and add a little paint. Whisk well with the fork to make a paste.

4 Arrange the sheets of newspaper into a pile, and place a sheet of paper on top. Brush the vinegar and sugar paste across the paper. Notice how the bubbles leave an interesting pattern. Leave the paper for about five minutes, to allow the paste to set slightly.

5 Draw a pattern in the paste with a small piece of thick card or with a card comb (a piece of card with notches cut into one end).

6 Papers patterned using vinegar and sugar paste.

7 If you add more sugar to your paste mix, the designs, when dry, will have a shinier finish.

8 Another idea for a
vinegar and sugar
paste design.

Roller patterned papers

Another method of making patterned paper is to apply colour with a printing roller.

You will need a plastic sheet, acrylic paints, a printing roller, and paper.

1 Put a little colour on to the plastic sheet. Charge the roller with colour and roll it across the paper. Use several colours for your pattern.

2 A colourful rollered paper.

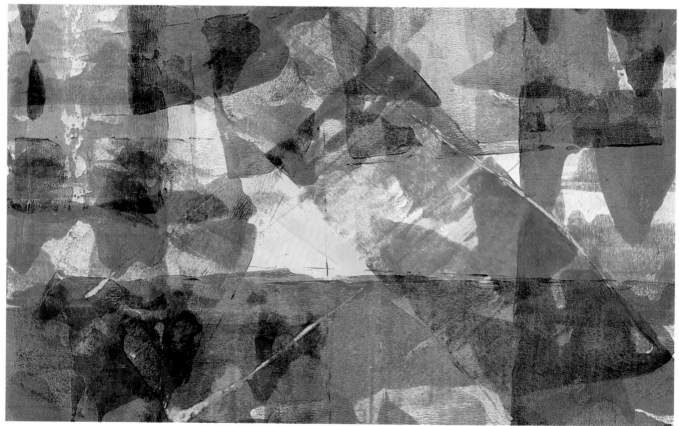

A greetings card

To make this card you will need thin white card, a pencil, a craft knife, a metal ruler, scissors, a sheet of roller patterned paper, and glue.

3 Cut a square window in the centre of a postcard-sized piece of card. Use this as a frame to help you select an interesting section of patterned paper. Using the inside edges of the frame as guidelines, draw around the edges of the patterned square you have chosen.

4 Fold another piece of card in half to make a basic greetings card shape. Mark and cut out a square window in the front of the greetings card. The window should be the same size as the square on the patterned paper. Cut out the patterned square leaving a 1cm border around the edges. Glue around this border (on the patterned side of the paper). Stick the patterned square on to the window of the greetings card so that the pattern shows through and becomes the picture on the front of the card.

5 The finished card accompanies a parcel wrapped in the rest of the roller patterned paper. Notice the matching gift tag on the parcel, too. Your gift tag can be made from a folded or unfolded piece of card. Punch a hole at one end for the tie.

Stencilled patterns and pictures are created by applying colour to a stencil sheet from which a design has been cut. When the sheet is removed, the coloured stencil print remains.

You will need pieces of sponge, boiled linseed oil, thin white card, a pencil, paper, carbon paper, a craft knife, a metal ruler, a flat-headed brush, paints, adhesive pads, felt-tip pens, and scissors.

Making a stencil sheet

1 Using a piece of sponge, apply a little linseed oil to the surface of a sheet of white card. As the oil is absorbed, the card will become translucent. Leave to dry.

A bird stencil

2 Draw a picture on a sheet of paper. Keep the shape of your picture fairly simple, with strong, clear lines.

3 Place a sheet of carbon paper (carbon side down) over the oiled stencil sheet. Now place your picture on top. Draw over the lines of your picture carefully and firmly. The carbon will transfer the lines to the stencil sheet.

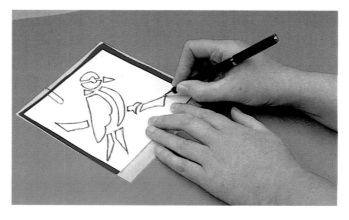

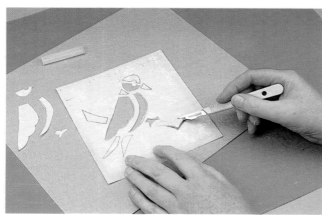

4 Using the craft knife, carefully cut around the outline of the design as it appears on the stencil sheet.

Leave some card 'bridges' between the sections, to strengthen the design.

5 Place the stencil on a sheet of paper. Using the flat-headed brush and only a little colour, dab paint through the stencil.

6 A repeat pattern can be made. Remember to wipe the stencil sheet clean before repeating a stencil, or before changing the colour.

Making a 3-D card

7 Cut out one of your stencilled pictures and attach two adhesive pads to the back.

8 Make a basic greetings card shape from a piece of card. Glue a piece of coloured paper on to the front of the card, if you wish, for added effect. Press the cut-out stencilled picture on to the front of the card. The adhesive pads raise the picture above the surface of the card, to give a 3-D effect.

9 Use felt-tip pens to add some more decorations to your design.

10 The finished card.

A folded symmetrical design

11 Cut a square from thin white card, fold it three times as shown, and cut small pieces from the folded edges.

12 Carefully unfold the cut square to reveal the symmetrical pattern.

13 Use a piece of sponge to dab colour on to your stencil. Use very little paint so that it does not run under the edges of the stencil.

14 The sponge gives a soft, mottled effect.

15 A repeat symmetrical pattern.

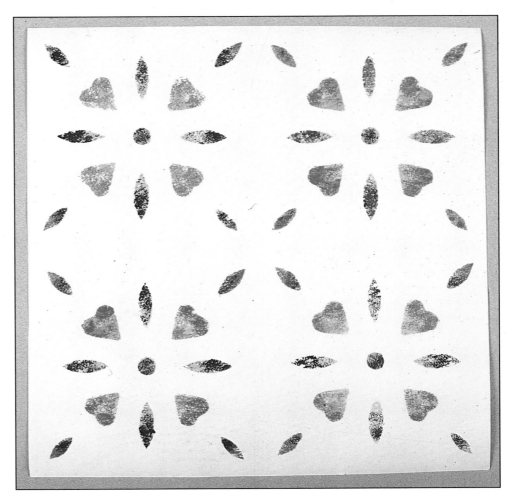

Splatter designed papers

In this method of paper decoration, the outlines of shapes are shown by splattering paint around their edges. This creates a 'negative' image in which the shapes remain uncoloured. Compare this to the 'positive' images formed by the stencilling process (see pages 17-23), where the design itself is coloured.

You will need a large cardboard box, paper, some leaves, paints, an old brush, and a stick.

1 Stand the cardboard box upright on the table, with the opening towards you. Work 'inside' the box, as shown, in order to protect your work **area**. Place a sheet of **paper** inside the box, and arrange a few leaves on the paper. Charge the brush with paint. Splatter the paint around the leaves by gently drawing the stick towards you across the bristles of the brush.

2 The finished effect.

3 *An Autumn Leaf.*

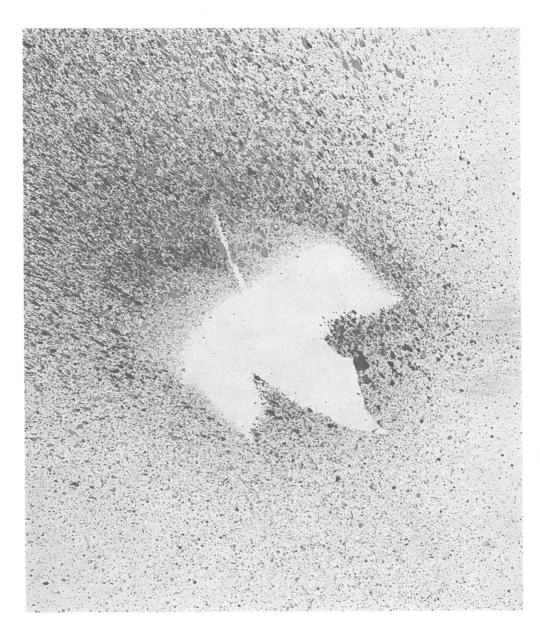

Sprayed decorative papers

A second way of splattering colour is by diffusion.

You will need paper, a diffuser spray, coloured inks, and an iron. You will also need to cover your work table and any nearby walls or furniture with old newspaper, for protection.

4 Crumple a piece of paper, then open it out so that the creases are still bumpy. Use the diffuser to spray ink across the paper.

The ink will cover the surfaces which face you but will not touch the areas which face away from you.

5 Turn the paper around and spray again, using a second colour.

6 Leave the paper to dry, then iron it.

7 *Mystical Mountains.*
An ironed sprayed
paper using just one
colour.

8 Try this method of splattering colour again. This time fold a piece of paper, concertina fashion. Open the paper out, so that the concertina folds stand up. Spray ink across the folds …

9 … then turn the paper around so that the opposite sides of the folds face you. Spray again, using a second colour.

10 The finished paper, ironed. The sprayed ink makes the paper seem as if it is still folded.

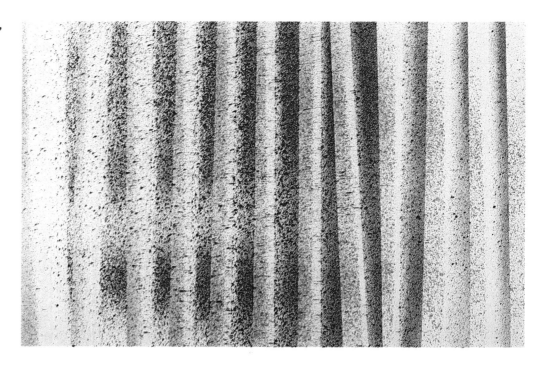

11 Sprayed paper which was folded in a fan shape.

12 A small gift wrapped as a cracker, with a matching card. To make the card, cut a strip from the sprayed paper, fold it in a concertina and glue it to the front of the card so the the folds stand out and create a 3-D effect.

Screen printed papers

Screen printing is another way of decorating papers using a stencil. Ink is forced through a material screen, and a coloured print is made around the stencil design.

You will need a pencil, paper, scissors, a screen printing frame and squeegee, and water-based printing inks.

1 Draw a design on a sheet of paper. Here a symmetrical design is being made on folded paper.

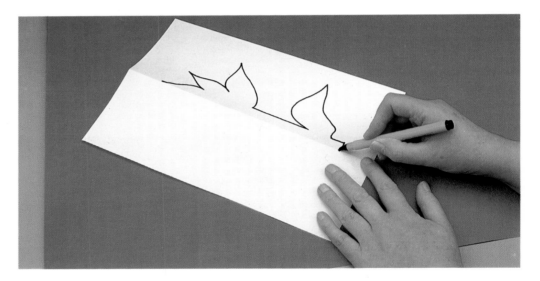

2 Cut out the design. This cut-out shape is your stencil.

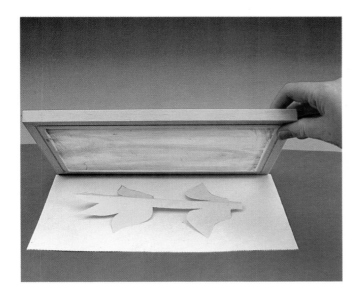

3 Lay the stencil on top of the sheet of paper which is to be printed, and place the screen on top.

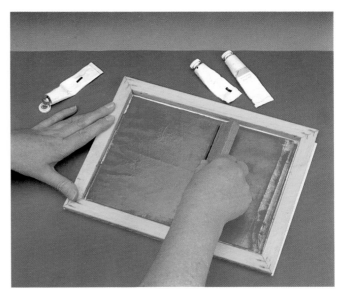

4 Squeeze some ink along one edge of the screen. Press the squeegee firmly against the screen and draw it across, taking the colour with it.

5 Lift the screen to reveal the print. The area without colour is in the shape of the stencil.

6 A selection of screen prints. The print on the bottom right was made by using the cut-out design *(top right)* as the stencil.

7 To make a two-colour print, wash the screen with water and prepare a second stencil by cutting away more shapes from the basic design. Allow the first colour to dry before applying the second colour over the original print.

8 A finished two-colour print.

Sponge printed papers

Decorating papers with a sponge printing block is easy and fun.

You will need pieces of sponge, scissors, card, glue, paints, paper and glitter.

1 Experiment first with a small piece of sponge. Print with each of the sponge's edges in turn. Do the results you achieve vary? Try curling one of the edges to obtain a curved pattern.

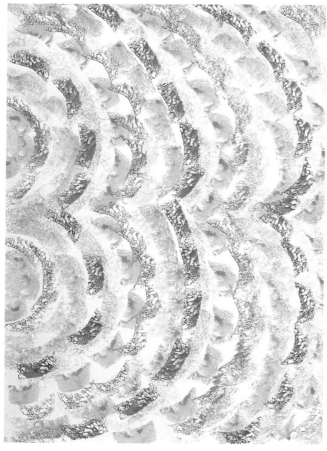

2 A sponge printed design.

3 Another colourful pattern.

4 Cut some shapes from the pieces of sponge. Glue each shape on to a piece of card. Leave to dry. These are your printing blocks.

5 Charge the sponge shapes with paint, and print on to a sheet of paper. Using very little paint gives a pleasing, mottled effect.

6 Try adding glitter to your decorated paper while the paint is still wet.

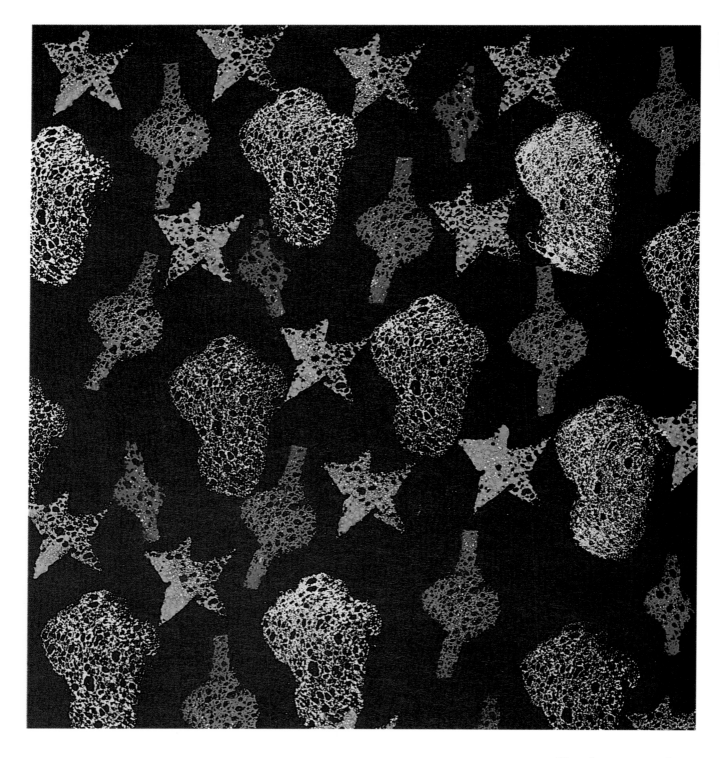

7 *Clouds, Stars and Planets.* The finished paper.

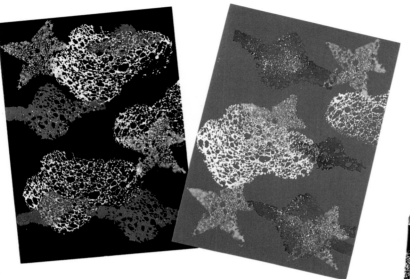

8 Make greetings cards using the same method. Try printing on different coloured papers.

9 An individually printed paper makes a lovely surprise for your friends and relations.

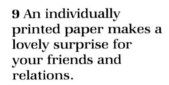

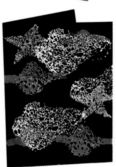

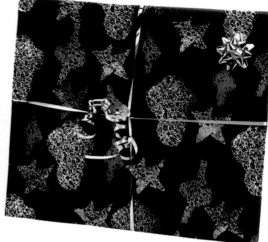

10 Use a sponge block to print a set of small cards. Use these as gift tags or as place settings at a party.

Marbling inks are oil-based colours and are often used in the art of decorative paper making.

You will need a tray of water, marbling inks, a thin stick, sheets of paper, and wallpaper paste.

1 Drip a few spots of marbling colour on to the surface of the water. With the tip of the stick, gently swirl the colours into a pattern.

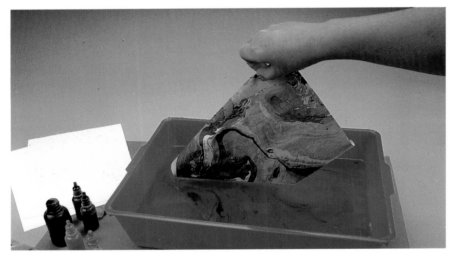

2 Lay a sheet of paper over the water, then lift it out carefully. Leave to dry.

3 If you wish to control the spread of colours in your pattern, add some wallpaper paste to the water. Leave to thicken (it should be the consistency of thin cream), then drip some drops of marbling colour on to the surface of the paste.

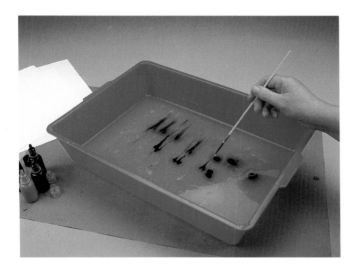

4 Draw the tip of the stick across the colours, first in one direction …

5 … then in the other direction.

6 Lay a sheet of paper over the surface …

7 … then lift the paper.

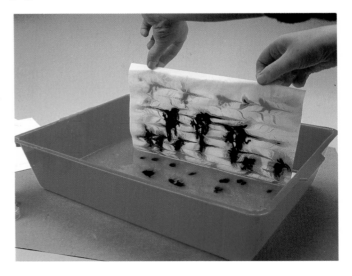

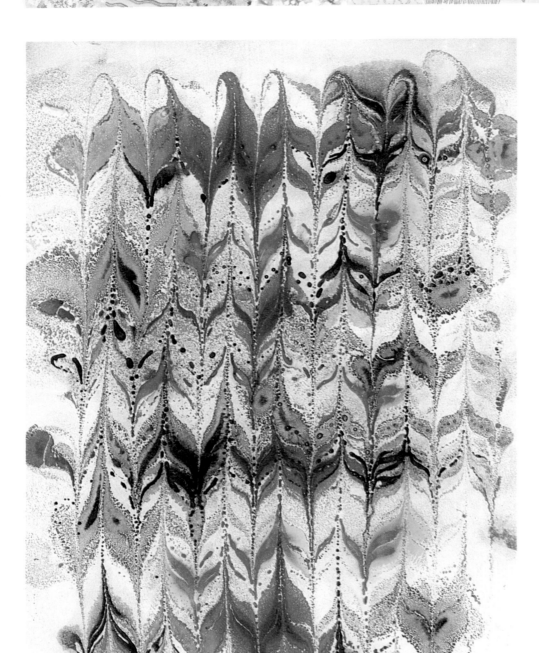

8 A feathered design.
The wallpaper paste
prevents the colours
from spreading.

9 Experiment with different colours to produce your own marbled design.

10 A small box covered with marbled paper makes an attractive container for a small gift. Make a greetings card to accompany your gift by mounting a section of your marbled paper on to a piece of thin card.

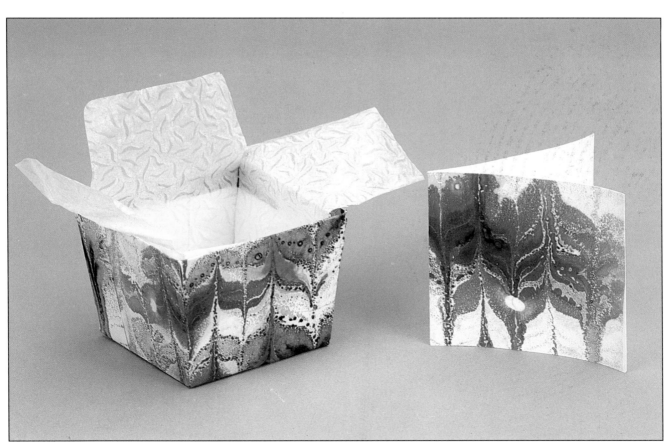

Dipped and dyed papers

Attractive decorated papers can be made by folding and dyeing. In this way, plain white paper serviettes or kitchen towels can be transformed into colourful party table napkins!

You will need paper serviettes or kitchen towels, and a selection of different coloured inks or cold-water dyes.

1 Prepare your serviettes or kitchen towels by folding them in different ways – into squares or triangles, for example, or by twisting, rolling or pleating. Dip one end of a folded paper into the ink or dye, then lift it out quickly so that only a little colour is absorbed. Repeat by dipping the other end of the paper, then the middle.

2 Leave to dry, then unfold gently.

3 An attractive place setting for a party. As well as being arranged decoratively in the glasses, the patterned serviettes can also be used as place mats.

4 Notice the sponge printed place setting cards and the gifts wrapped in home-made decorated paper. Happy birthday!

Here are a few more activities for you to try.

A decorated paper book cover

1 Use decorated papers to make a cover for a book or folder. Use two sheets of thick card and cover them carefully with two of your decorated sheets. Punch two holes at one end of each cover and make a string tie to hold the pages.

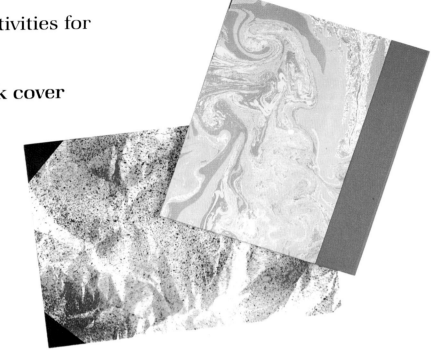

Your own notepaper

2 Prepare a tray of marbling colour. Dip one edge of a sheet of paper into the water and lift it out. The marbling colour will make an attractive border on both sides of your notepaper.

3 Repeat for the other three edges.

4 You can make a set of matching notepaper by using the same tray of ink.

An envelope for a greetings card or sheet of notepaper

5 Select a sheet of decorated paper. Here, a sheet of marbled paper has been chosen. Fold and cut an envelope to fit your greetings card or notepaper, as shown. Make the envelope slightly larger than the card so that the card will slip in and out easily.

6 You may wish to have the marbled pattern on the inside of your envelope.

7 Fold the bottom flap up, and glue it to the side flaps of the envelope. Use a white sticky label for the name if necessary.

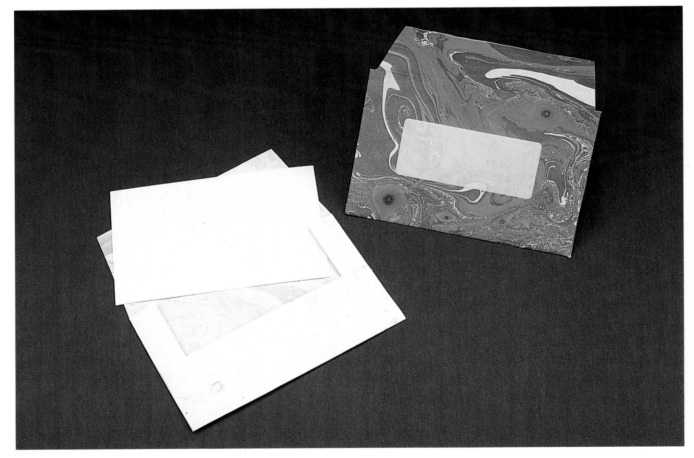

Most of the materials mentioned in this book are easy to obtain.

Paper and card
Most stationers stock a good range of paper and card in different weights and colours.

Printing inks
Some recommended water-based inks are: Arnold Multiprint; Berol Print Inks; Reeves Block Printing Watercolours.

Printing rollers
These are obtainable in a variety of widths. A width of 10cm is an average size and is recommended for the activities in this book.

Specialist materials
Specialist materials such as marbling inks, boiled linseed oil and printing rollers can be obtained from an artists' materials stockist or ordered through a schools' supplier such as:

NOTTINGHAM EDUCATIONAL SUPPLIES, Ludlow Hill Road, West Bridgeforth, Nottingham NG2 6HD.

Scoring card
If you want to fold a piece of card so that the folded edge is straight and neat, you should 'score' the card first. Place the piece of card flat on a cutting board, and position a metal ruler on the card so that one of its long edges follows exactly the line of the fold you want to make. Hold a craft knife in your 'work' hand, blade pointing downwards, and hold the ruler down firmly with your other hand. Run the craft knife firmly down the edge of the metal ruler which lies along the fold line, cutting *into* the card as you do so but not cutting *through* it. Once a piece of card has been 'scored' in this way, you will find it easier to fold the card in the way you want.